The Three Goats

The Three Goats

Margaret Hillert

illustrated by Mel Pekarsky

𝒇 Follett Publishing Company   Chicago

Library of Congress Catalog Card Number: 63-9616

ISBN 0-695-48720-5 Titan binding   ISBN 0-695-88720-3 Trade binding   151617/807978

See the goats.

One, two, three goats.

Goats can run and jump.

The little goat said, "I want something.

I want to find something.

Away I go."

See the goat go.

The little goat can go up.

Up, up, up.

Look down here.

Here is something funny.

Run, run, run.

Jump, jump, jump.

Here I go.

Little goat, you can not go.

I want you, little goat.

Here I come.

Not I, not I.

Oh, help, help.

Away I go.

Jump, jump, jump.

Oh my, oh my.

See the little goat run away.

Here I come.

I want something.

I can come up here.

Goat, goat.

Come down.

Come down to me.

I want you.

Not I, not I.

I can run away.

Run, run, run.

And jump, jump, jump.

18

Oh my, oh my.

The goat can run and jump.

The goat can run away.

Big goat wants something.

See the big, big goat.

Here I come.

Here I come.

I see you, big goat.

I want you.

Come down here.

Not I.

You can not make me come down.

Come up here to me.

Look, big goat, look.

Here I come for you.

And—

Here you go!

Down.

Down.

Down.

See here.

See here.

We can run.

We can jump.

We can play.

We can run and play.

Follett JUST Beginning-to-Read Books

Uses of these books. These books are planned for the very youngest readers, those who have been learning to read for about six to eight weeks and who have a small preprimer reading vocabulary. The books are written by Margaret Hillert, a first-grade teacher in the Royal Oak, Michigan, schools. Each book is illustrated in full color.

Children will have a feeling of accomplishment in their first reading experiences with these delightful books that *they can read.*

The Three Goats

Attractive and amusing pictures of the old story of the Billy Goats Gruff, with a text that uses 36 preprimer words.

Word List

7	see		want	**13**	you
	the		something		not
	goats		to		come
	one		find		
	two		away	**14**	oh
	three		go		help
	can	**9**	up	**15**	my
	run				
	and			**17**	me
	jump	**10**	look		
			down	**20**	big
			here		
				23	make
8	little				
	said		is	**24**	for
	I		funny		
				27	play